Black Country Pits

above and below ground and what they were really like

by

A.J.R. Hickling

FOREWORD

W.K.V. Gale

It was two major natural resources - coal and iron ore - and three lesser but still vital ones - limestone, clay and sand - on which the industrial development of the Black Country was founded. All these minerals were abundant, at shallow depths or in some cases on the surface and therefore cheap to produce. Elihi Burrit, in *Walks in the Black Country and its Green Borderland* (1868), summed up the position adequately when he said 'Nature did all she could for the ironmasters of the Black Country; indeed, everything except literally building the furnaces themselves'.

Coal was the fuel for smelting and processing iron (and later, steel) and for firing the boilers of countless steam engines; limestone was the flux used in smelting, the refractory bricks of which the furnaces were built were made from local clay; and sand was needed for moulding and casting. And the coal and iron industries were to a large extent interdependent. Just as iron needed coal, so the mines required many items made of iron or steel; steam winding and pumping engines, boilers, miners' tools and horseshoes are just a few examples.

Many other industries developed, too, on the abundant supplies of iron and coal. Chains are an example and the mines were important users of chains. They included some specially developed locally for mining. For example, flat or 'rattle' chain, used for winding, was patented in 1844 by H.P Parkes of Tipton.

By the middle of the 19th century the Black Country coal and iron trades were prosperous and the future seemed secure. It was said, foolishly, that the mineral resources were 'Inexhaustible'. They were not. It has also been said that the heavy industries declined because the coal seams were exhausted. This is also untrue.

Coal was present in the ratio of roughly 15 to 1 compared with iron ore and it was the ore which was worked out first. Even as early as 1845 some blast furnaces in the Black Country were drawing their iron ore from North Staffordshire and there was some internal traffic in ores from exhausted areas to those where supplies were still available. There were some shortages of coal in a few places; but on the whole it was still abundant.

So, from the 1850's the iron trade started its slow decline, production moving to other localities where the ore was readily available. Coal production continued, though the demand inevitably fell off as the ironworks closed. Today, of course, mining too is no more. There is still plenty of coal in the Black Country but it is not possible to mine it by modern methods.

A.J.R. Hickling 1989

BLACK COUNTRY PITS.

by A. J. R. HICKLING

The underground working of Black Country pits for coal has now completely ceased and is never likely to be resumed in the future. Not only that but also the winding engines, engine houses and chimneys have all disappeared and in fact most of the old spoil mounds have been levelled and are now built upon.

At this present time practically nothing remains of any relics of these pits, and I can only think of the Old Cobbs pumping engine house which is now only a shell, the New Hawne winding engine house, and the fan engine from the Cuba pit at Gornal which I acquired and restored and have working occasionally on live steam.

Yet when I was a small boy there were literally hundreds of pits in the Black Country all busy and turning out coal and fireclay as fast as possible. This book contains many photographs which represent the type of pits you would see in byegone days and constitutes a unique collection of scenes both above and below ground. Some of these photographs go back to about 1875 and on the front cover is a pit on the Burton Road at Upper Gornal which was working until about 1950.

In the Black Country there were 4 main seams

1. Brooch about 3'6" thick
2. Thick coal about 30ft. thick.
3. Heathen coal about 4ft. thick.
4. Fireclay.

The brooch coal outcropped a good deal in the Lower Gornal area and it was probably these outcrops that led to the development of the iron industry in this area because in many cases it did not involve any underground working and could be obtained from the surface. As this became exhausted it led to the formation of what are called Bell Pits, these were just a single shaft and as the coal was worked from them it was belled out as far as was safe. These were later supplanted by sinking 2 shafts and drawing the bad air up one of these which was called the upcast and of course this became the general practice in all mining.

Black Country Pits were very unpredictable to work in and there were many accidents caused by rock falls and ironstone boulders. They were extremely wet and a reference to the Mines Drainage Commission Report of 1920 shows that for every ton of coal raised 40 tons of water had to be pumped out, the wages paid to miners were very low indeed and the work was extremely hard and under conditions which would not be tolerated today.

Most of the Black Country pits were very shallow and coal outcropped at the surface, many of them perhaps only 50 or 60 yards deep and 200 - 250 yards would be quite deep by Black Country standards, another factor was the uneven quality of the coal measures which were heavily faulted and often times difficult to extract.

Ventilation underground left much to be desired. Most of the smaller pits were ventilated by a steam jet in the upcast shaft which by warming the air would cause a current of fresh air to enter the down cast shaft and circulate around the workings and then by passed out of the up-cast shaft and I can only remember 3 or 4 pits that were ventilated by means of an exhaust fan driven by a fan engine.

The actual working of the coal was carried out with picks and shovels and it was loaded into 4 wheeled tubs of 8 to 10cwts capacity which were pulled to the pit bottom by ponies.

The lighting was by means of tallow candles which were stuck in a ball of clay, and really I cannot think of any occupation as dirty and debilitating and dangerous as working down a Black Country pit.

During my eighty years I spent many hours visiting and descending pits in the Black Country and I suppose I developed a morbid fascination for them, but these are scenes which will never be seen again.

Today if you go down Lea Hall Colliery at Rugeley you will see fluorescent lighting right to the coalface and the coal is ripped out by huge coal cutters and falls onto a conveyor belt which will take it right to a junction about 1/4 mile from the pit bottom and there it falls into big mine cars and then transported by electric locomotives and pushed hydraulically onto the cage but I think that if you look through the various pages in this book which are all produced from actual photographs that are in my possession you will get a good idea of what Black Country pits were really like.

This is No. 6 Pit on Fosters Field now part of the L.C.P. Estate, Pensnett.
It is an old rattlechain pit and standing disused.

Note. The small diameter pulleys over which the chain passed. The chain also passes over jockey pulleys. It is particularly interesting because it shows the whole pit complete.

Note. The horse gin at the back which would be used for getting men out of the pit if the engine failed.

This is a picture of No. 17 at Shut End, Pensnett and although the engine and engine house were demolished many years ago the small round chimney on the right hand side of the engine house remained there for many years and was only demolished about 16 years ago.
This picture shows the beam winding engine and rattle chain drums.

No 15 pit L.C.P. Estate near Stallings Lane.
This pit I remember as a small boy and I saw it being demolished in about 1916.
The chain on the full drum consists of 3 chains with oblong links and to give greater strength oak wedges were hammered into the long links to hold the three chains together.
They were called Rattle Chain Pits because of the noise made by these during the process of winding.
There were no wire ropes in those days.

These 3 photographs show the Earl of Dudley's Himley Colliery No.8. near the mineral line off Ham Lane.

They were taken in 1929 and the pit ceased working in about 1919.

The thick coal was 143 yd. deep. In the left hand photograph are the 2 egg ended boilers and in the middle photograph the author is seen sitting on the engine bed.

It is to be noticed that the engine had a one to three gearing and the 2 winding drums are different in size the outer drum would be for tanking water out of the upcast shaft and the inner drum would be the drawing shaft for the coal, on the extreme right can be seen the brake drum for the engine.

The Earl of Dudley built quite a number of winding engines in this particular style at Castle Mill Works.

This is the winding engine house of the Cuba Pit at Gornal, the farthest shaft was purely for water and ventilation and the first shaft was for drawing coal.

I went down this pit many times, it was 80 yards in depth and extremely wet.

It was worked until about 1945.

There were a pair of winding engines which were geared and very much over their job.

This was a Gin Pit on the Burton Road at Upper Gornal where the Ambulance Station now is.

It worked for many years and the tubs were pulled up by a horse travelling in a circle around the rope drum.

The remains of a further derelict Gin Pit can be seen in the right hand corner.

This is a photograph of a Black Country pit with a shaft taking 2 cages and what appears to be a chimney is probably a ventilation duct for the entire pit and would have a furnace at the bottom of the upcast duct.

This is the interior of the winding engine house.

The engine has 2 cylinders with the winding drum in the middle.

This is a somewhat larger winding engine than was usually used in Black Country pits.

This is the same engine taken from the opposite end of the engine house showing the engine man carrying out his work.

This engine would have twin cylinders.

This photograph was taken of coal pickers in the 1912 strike and shows a typical coal wharf scene.

This was usually the manner in which coal wharves were constructed and it is seen that the local Police Constable was there and also the various lengths of timber are there for making into pit props.

This photograph was probably the Corbyn's Hall Colliery at Pensnett.

The Corbyn Hall Company had a number of pits so it could have been any one of them.

123
COAL. PICKING.
COAL STRIKE MAR 1912

This is a canal wharf where coal would be unloaded from the pit and roughly sorted into size and then sent away in boats.

This was a typical scene of the surface of a pit and was probably one of Bassano's pits at Rowley Regis.

Note the beam winding engine used to work the two shafts.

John Hall (Stourbridge) Limited. No. 2. pit at Amblecote.

A photograph taken about 1960 when it was still actively working but all this area was later opencast to remove any remaining coal or fireclay

A typical blacksmiths shop at a colliery.

The blacksmith was an important man because each day he had to sharpen all the picks as well as shoeing all the horses at the pit and carrying out much smithy work that was always required at a colliery.

Blacksmith on left and the assistant holding sledge hammer on the right.

This is the pit bottom where cages would haul up the full tubs and lower the empty ones and it is noted that this is also the end of the haulage where the tub could be detached and pushed onto the cage.

The full tubs are pushed onto the cage at the right hand side, the empty tubs which are then pushed along the right hand side of the photo around the cage and traverse to the haulage station.

This is the underground office where the Deputies would gather to fill in their report books for the day and it will be noticed that there is also a signalling point over the door.

It will also be seen that each Deputy carries a stick and also a safety lamp.

The engine here which is the haulage engine for the pit is a gas engine and it is near the pit bottom and probably exhausts into the chimney stack referred to on page 8.

This takes the tubs to the pit bottom.

This is the jig wheel at the top of a jig bank and it would allow a full tub going to the haulage to pull up an empty tub to replace it.

The speed of this haulage is governed by the brake wheel which can be seen in the middle of the picture.

This picture is of an air door which would act together with another one to make an air lock near to the pit bottom and the purpose of it is to force the air around the workings instead of going straight into the upcast shaft.

A photograph of a haulage junction.

The empty tubs would go down the rails on the right hand side and the full ones would come up on the left hand side and into the main road.

The Dialler (or Surveyor) is setting out a new road and it is notable that he has a boy on the right hand side holding a lamp to a point directed by the Surveyor, who is dialling the road.

This is a hand worked coal face.

The coal can be seen on the left hand side, the right hand side has already been worked and they are getting the face ready to extract it by advancement into the seam.

The only light appears to be the safety lamp hanging above the man with the shovel.

This is an interesting photograph taken in 1869 of a haulage road getting very near to the face of the coal and it will be seen by the condition of the steel joists and the timber that the work there is very rough.

This illustrates hand holing at the coal face, the pikemen are under cutting the seam which is spragged up.
The Deputy with the lamp and the stick is overseeing the work and when the coal has been cut the spraggs will be removed and the coal can then be wedged down.
There is a candle to be seen in the right hand corner of the picture.

The coal has now been cut and the pikeman is getting it down ready for loading into a tub which is seen on the left hand side of the Deputy.

This photograph is a continuation of the previous one where the coal has been holed out and the pikeman now is getting it down while the roof is supported by the upright prop with a flat piece of timber on top of it.

This man is enlarging the road way because the coal has reduced its thickness and the actual seam of coal can be seen in the background of the picture. circa 1875
Note the hand drilling machine in the picture.

These small photographs were taken by the author down the Cuba Pit at Gornal.
The first one shows a pit road leading to the face.

The second one shows the heathen coal face holed out and with a spragg underneath it ready to drop the coal.

The third one shows a cog which was really a mix of pit props lying horizontally with pieces of stone between them. The purpose being to hold up a bad section of the roof.
These photographs were taken about 1929.